A HUNDRED AC

a study of a hundred acres of Britain throughout one year

~ Freddie McKeown ~

Printed in England. ISBN 0 85503 165 4

January ~ the stream

An eerie shriek tells the foxes' plight
down by the stream on a frosty night.
On snow-dusted tracks, cold paws sink,
maybe an otter, a stoat or a mink?
In an iced moon sky, winter moths drift;
for food, in the alders, the siskins sift.
Hungry and cold, they all forage for food ~
by the stream, on the bank and in Alder Wood.

The stream
THE RIVER
alders

winter moth

early moth

alder false cone

siskins

stoat

the stream

mink

fox

otter

February ~ the rookery and grass pond

Rooks will start nesting, for twigs they will seek,
late in the month, if the weather's not bleak.
Up in the trees nests the mistle thrush too,
a nest on the bank for the mallard will do.
We stroll to "grass pond", passing "big oak",
to see all the frog-spawn and hear the frog croak!
Of thousands of eggs just a few will survive,
escaping all hunters, tadpoles will thrive.

rook

mistle thrush

colts foot

lesser celandine

the rookery

common frog

mallards

male

frog-spawn

female

dragonfly nymphs and diving beetle larvae feed on frog-spawn

March ~ cormorant islands

On cormorant islands the flowers will stir –
primroses, marsh marigolds and mauve butterbur.
In search of some nectar, a big bumble bee
gathers the pollen from a flowering tree.
Goosanders will wander at water's edge,
whilst a cormorant watches on top of a hedge.
On sunny March days the butterflies soar,
and the birdsong's as loud as the rapids' roar.

peacock

goat
willow, sallow

honey bee

bumble bees

small
tortoiseshell

cormorant islands

cormorant

female

male
goosander

primroses

marsh marigold

butterbur

April ~ David's Lane

From White Farm to Pink House runs David's Lane,
bursting with flowers in showers of rain;
wild strawberry, archangel and small violet,
with speedwell and stitchwort gleam in the wet.
Robins and wrens nest on banks of the track...
Watch out for a hedgehog with spines on its back!
Bank voles or weasels or young rabbits run,
happy to romp in the spring morning sun!

robin

solitary bees

mining bee

mason bee

orange-tip butterfly

wren

white deadnettle

David's Lane

Yellow archangel

rabbit

wild strawberry

greater stitchwort

hedgehog

May ~ Scarp Wood

A blue haze of bluebells carpets the wood,
you may spot herb Paris if your eyesight is good!
Over eight playful cubs a vixen stands guard,
whilst down in her sett a badger digs hard.
The male buzzard circles looking for food
to take to his mate who waits on her brood.
The glorious sound of a woodpecker drummer
beats time for the season to change into summer.

buzzard

grey squirrel

nuthatches

great spotted woodpecker

bluebell glade, Scarp Wood

bluebells

herb Robert

herb paris

badger

vixen and her cubs

June ~ the river near the wetlands

On the swirling brown river the mute swans swim,
whilst under the surface some salmon skim.
From mud-hole homes young sand martins call,
grabbing for food they try not to fall!
Rest-harrow, musk mallow and monkey musk,
or hogweed as high as an elephant's tusk!
The setting sun makes the river glow red,
and sleep takes hold of the river bed.

sand martins

common sandpipers

giant hogweed

the river near the wetlands

musk mallow

salmon

mute swan

July ~ Alder Wood

Young chiffchaff, treecreeper, tit and goldcrest,
are ready to hunt so they leave the nest.
Insects and spiders are their favourite food,
now quick on the wing they scour the wood.
And if you sit still not making a sound,
you may hear small mammals scuttling round.
Under the leaves, or grass covered in dew,
hide wood mice, grey squirrels or maybe a shrew!

great tit

young chiffchaff

coal tit

goldcrest

common alder

tree creeper

over the fields to AlderWood

enchanter's nightshade

common shrew

nipplewort

red campion

wood mouse

August ~ the wetlands

A heron swoops down to catch a frog,
as it hops out of a wetland bog.
Greenshank, moorhen and sandpiper green,
down on this marshland can all be seen.
Thistles grow thick and their seeds are spread
by eager goldfinches who need to be fed.
Grass snake, smooth newt and dragonfly,
slither or swim or brightly fly by.

heron in
flight

greenshank

green
sand piper

welted
thistle

heron

goldfinches

the wetlands

moorhen

dragonfly

smooth newt

grass snake

September ~ the pastures

Mild autumn weather with milky white sun,
crossing the pasture a hare makes a run.
Warm moist conditions make fungi abound;
fat juicy earthworms come up from the ground.
A magpie, a pigeon, a rook or a crow,
a blustering pheasant flying too low.
Under the pasture a mole's out of sight,
and as the mist falls, the day turns to night.

pheasant

magpie

brown hare

grasshopper

the pastures

parasol mushrooms

field mushrooms

mole

common earthworm

October ~ Beech Bank

On a ridge by the river grow beeches and oaks,
which cold autumn rain now constantly soaks.
The leaves have changed colour, to russet and red,
mushrooms and toadstools poke through their leaf
bed.
A hedgehog is making a warm leafy nest,
now tired and ready for winter's long rest.
Acorns are gathered by squirrels and jays,
stocking their food stores for shortening days.

beech

jay

oak

blackberries

Beech Bank

acorns

milk cap fungi

hedgehog hibernating

hawthorn

November ~ the river

Down by the river the cold you can feel...
is there a gudgeon, a chub or an eel?
Nothing now stirs in waters so deep,
only small larvae on the river bed creep.
Perhaps they are hiding from kingfisher's sight...
he can dive from a branch or even in flight.
Up on the bank moves a solitary rat,
where in hot days of summer for picnics we sat.

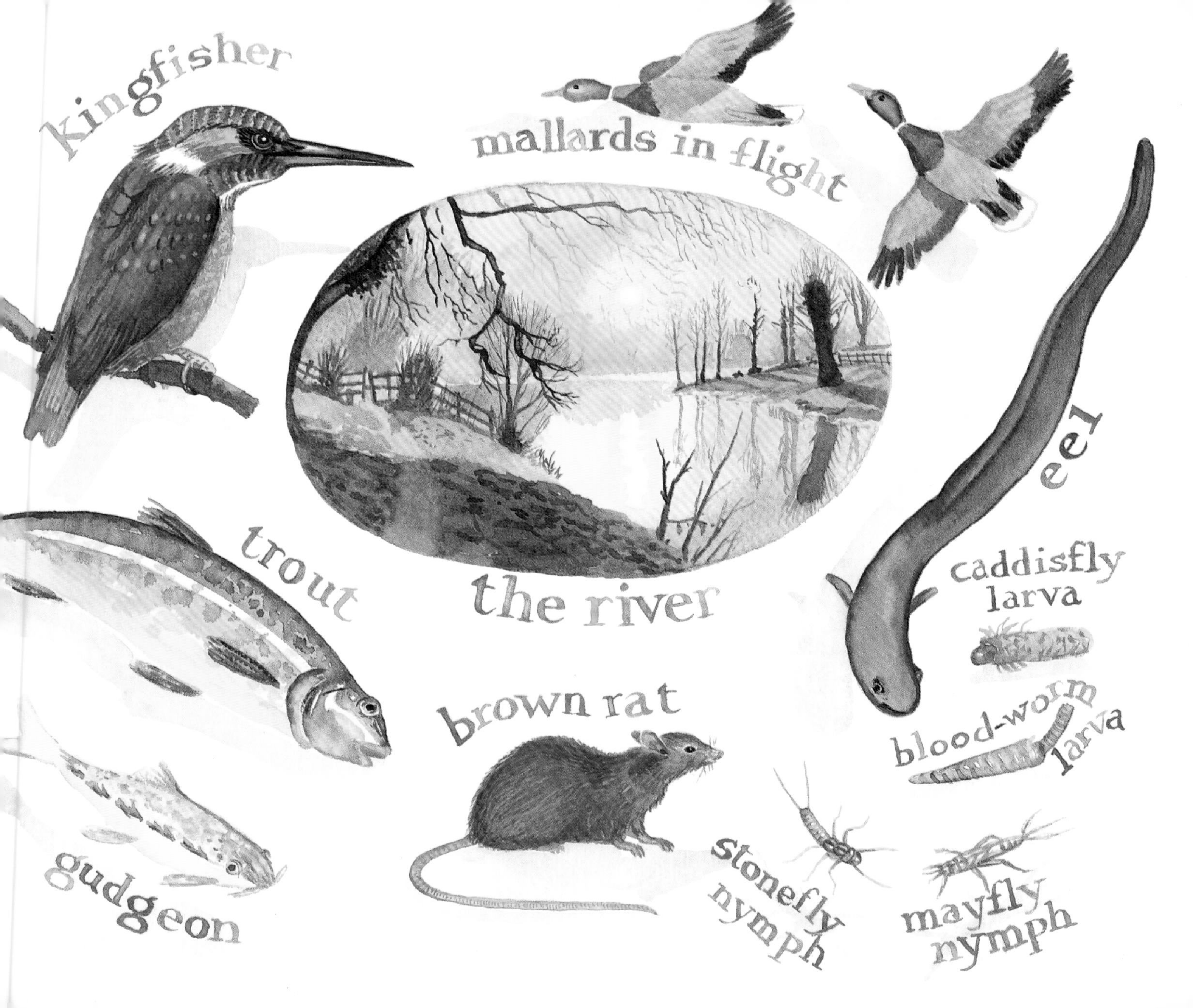

kingfisher

mallards in flight

the river

eel

caddisfly larva

trout

brown rat

blood-worm larva

gudgeon

stonefly nymph

mayfly nymph

December ~ around A Hundred Acres

Just before Christmas, the hoot of an owl
breaks through the silence, in weather that's foul.
In thick clumps of ivy, birds hide from the cold,
as long winter nights slowly unfold.
This is the month of festive good cheer,
but flooding and frost grasp the end of the year.